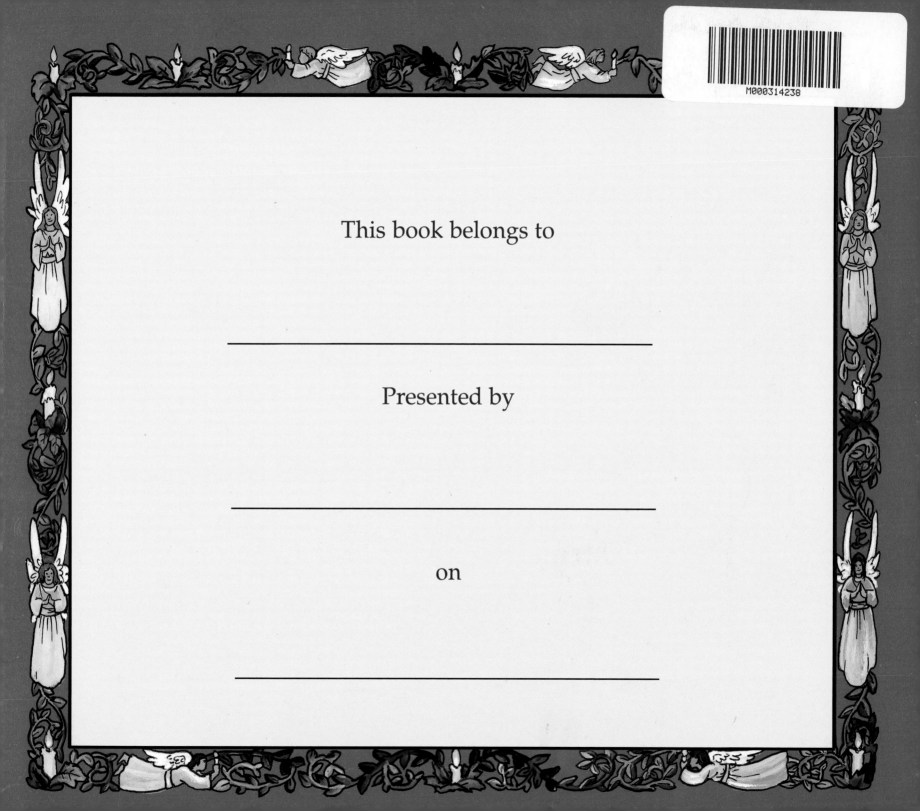

This book belongs to

_____

Presented by

_____

on

_____

Text copyright © 2000 Kelly A. Rainbolt
Illustrations copyright © 2000 Concordia Publishing House
Published by Concordia Publishing House
3558 S. Jefferson Avenue, St. Louis, MO 63118-3968
Manufactured in the United States of America

2   3   4   5   6   7   8   9   10   09   08   07   06   05   04   03   02   01   00

The Savior That God Sent

Kelly A. Rainbolt   Illustrated by Roberta Collier-Morales

This is baby Jesus all cozy and warm,
wrapped in blankets all tattered and torn.
He is the Savior that God sent.

This is the manger made out of lumber
that held baby Jesus as He lay down to slumber—
cozy and warm in blankets all torn ...

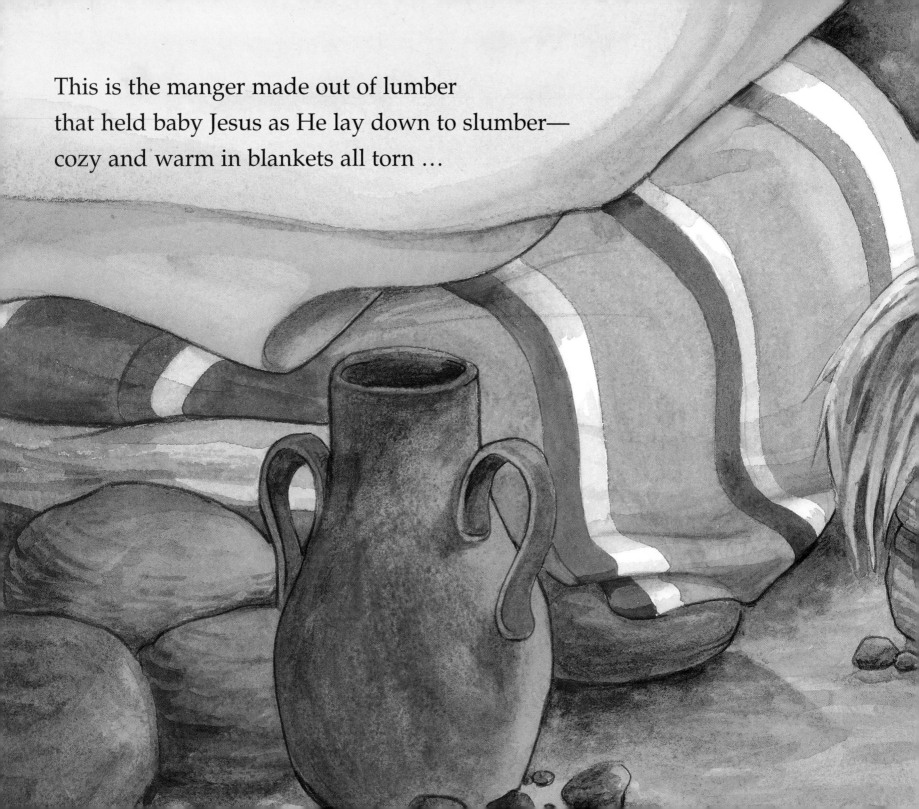

He is the Savior that God sent.

This is the stable where animals lived,
which was all the innkeeper had to give.
Inside was the manger made out of lumber
that held baby Jesus as He lay down to slumber—
cozy and warm in blankets all torn ...

He is the Savior that God sent.

This is the inn that was oh-so crowded,
filled with people who had come to be counted.
Out back was the stable where animals lived,
which was all the innkeeper had to give.
Inside was the manger made out of lumber
that held baby Jesus as He lay down to slumber—
cozy and warm in blankets all torn …

He is the Savior that God sent.

These are the parents, Joseph and Mary,
with all the things they could possibly carry.
They had come on a donkey to an inn oh-so crowded,
that was filled with people who had come to be counted.
Out back was a stable where animals lived,
which was all the innkeeper had to give.
Inside was a manger made out of lumber
that held baby Jesus as He lay down to slumber—
cozy and warm in blankets all torn …

He is the Savior that God sent.

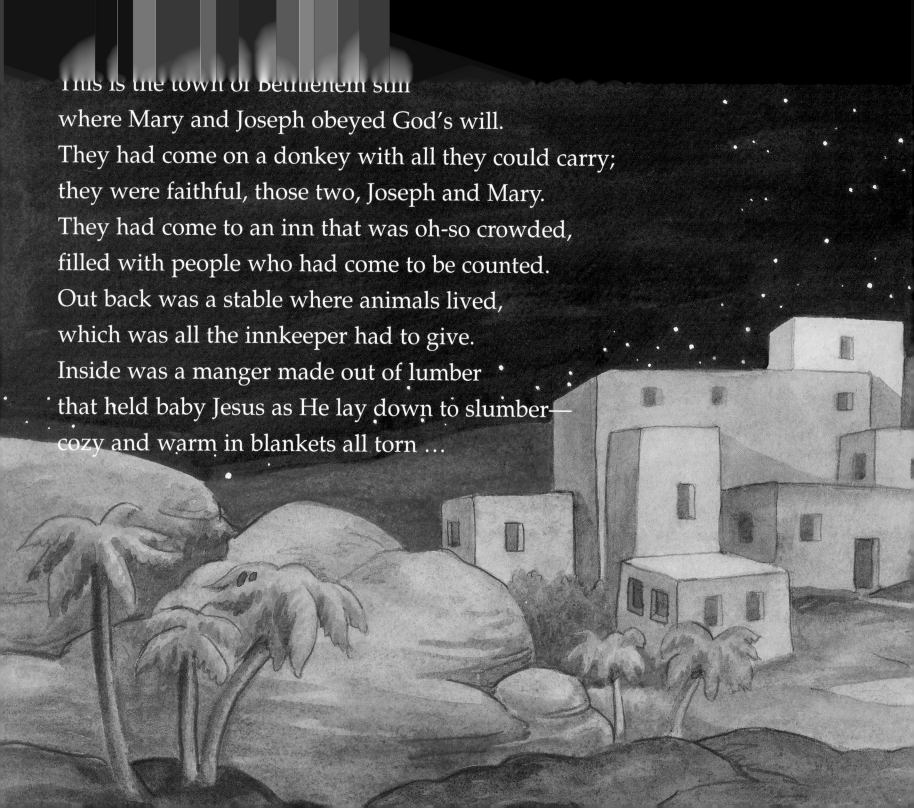

This is the town of Bethlehem still
where Mary and Joseph obeyed God's will.
They had come on a donkey with all they could carry;
they were faithful, those two, Joseph and Mary.
They had come to an inn that was oh-so crowded,
filled with people who had come to be counted.
Out back was a stable where animals lived,
which was all the innkeeper had to give.
Inside was a manger made out of lumber
that held baby Jesus as He lay down to slumber—
cozy and warm in blankets all torn …

He is the Savior that God sent.

These are the shepherds who saw quite a sight
as the nighttime sky became so bright.
An angel appeared with news of great joy—the birth of a Savior—a baby boy.
To the still town of Bethlehem that night,
the shepherds came running with all of their might—
right past the inn that was oh-so crowded,
filled with people who had come to be counted.
Out back was the stable where animals lived,
which was all the innkeeper had to give.
Then in the manger made out of lumber,
they found baby Jesus as He lay down to slumber—
cozy and warm in blankets all torn …
They found the Savior that God sent.